$18.00   c.1

The Statue of Liberty

DATE DUE

2-9 x9			

Reading Essentials
in Social Studies

SYMBOLS OF A NATION

The Statue of Liberty

Thomas S. Owens and Diana Star Helmer

Perfection Learning®

For another grand lady, LoRae Porter, friend of cats.

Editorial Director: Susan C. Thies
Editor: Mary L. Bush
Book Design: Jill M. Kline and Tobi S. Cunningham
Cover Design: Mike Aspengren

1   2   3   4   5   BA   06   05   04   03   02

ISBN 0-7891-5869-8

TABLE OF CONTENTS

1. The Greatest Gift 4

2. 'Tis Better to Give 8

3. Carving Out a Place 12

4. Big Dreams 15

5. Starting Small 18

6. Supporting the Dream 23

7. I Lift My Lamp 29

8. The Tests of Time 34

9. Liberty Unafraid 38

   Internet Connections to the Statue of Liberty . . 43

   GLOSSARY 44

   INDEX 47

Chapter One

The Greatest Gift

Liberty isn't something that you can see or touch. So how could an artist make a statue of liberty?

Liberty is one of the most important ideas in the world. Liberty is freedom. It means being able to choose what you do, how you act, and what you say. Liberty is the ability to change—or not to change, if you choose. Liberty is so important that people all over the world throughout history have died trying to get it.

The Statue of Liberty was created to honor and remember those who have fought for liberty.

America and France Unite

The first people from England to settle in America were not free. These colonists were ruled by the English king, even though they didn't live in England anymore. The king wanted to make laws for the colonists. He wanted them to pay taxes to support England. The king wanted America, the new world, to be just like the old world of England.

King George of England

The colonists, however, had moved to America to escape the old world. They had new ideas about what kinds of laws were best. They didn't want to give all of their money to the king. So they decided to fight the king of England for their liberty.

The colonists from England had help in this fight. French colonists didn't want the English king telling them what to do either. They also understood the English colonists' desire to free themselves from a king's rule.

France was another country ruled by kings. Like the English, many French people didn't like this system of government known as a monarchy. France had been controlled by kings for hundreds of years. French kings were famous for taxing farmers and other common people and then spending the money on castles and fancy clothes.

The Marquis de Lafayette

The idea of liberty was as exciting to many French people as it was to the English colonists. These French citizens believed that if they helped English colonists fight their king, then someday the Americans would help France fight its king.

General George Washington led the American fight against the British army. He was aided by the Marquis de Lafayette, a French soldier who convinced France to help the colonists.

General George Washington

Lafayette Lends a Hand to Liberty

Born in France, the Marquis de Lafayette became an orphan at age 12. When he was 14, he joined the army and became a soldier. In 1777, Lafayette went to Philadelphia and became friends with George Washington. The Frenchman then persuaded France to send help to the colonists fighting the American Revolutionary War.

The American Revolutionary War raged on from 1775 to 1783. In the end, the colonists won their freedom from England. They were granted the liberty they sought.

The Battle of Bunker Hill took place in June of 1775, during the first year of the American Revolutionary War.

Not long after, France had a **revolution** of its own. This was an even uglier war than the American Revolution. Eventually the French people found leaders who defeated the king. But soon the new leaders became unfair, power-hungry rulers too. France had still not found the liberty it was seeking.

Keep Dreaming

For almost a hundred years, the French people watched American **democracy** grow and wished that France would follow in America's footsteps. Many French people wanted to vote for laws like Americans did. They wanted to choose their leaders. Unfortunately, for many years, the French continued to dream of liberty while living under the control of powerful rulers.

As America neared its **centennial**, a small group of Frenchmen decided to celebrate. What if they sent a birthday present? It would have to be a marvelous gift. After all, America stood for liberty. The perfect present from France would let the world know that the French people still dreamed of freedom. It might cause more French people to think about liberty as well.

Giving America a present would also help keep America's friendship. France would continue to need America's help in its fight for freedom. And France would still need friendship when it finally did become free.

The group of Frenchmen decided that the present should celebrate liberty. They understood that liberty is a huge idea. That's why the Statue of Liberty was the largest statue in the world at the time it was built.

Liberty gives hope. Hope lets people see a better way. That's why the Statue of Liberty holds a torch to light the path to freedom.

On her head, Lady Liberty wears a crown with seven rays. This shows that liberty brings hope to the seven seas and seven continents of the world.

Lady Liberty holds a tablet with the date July 4, 1776, written on it. That was the day that America declared its independence from England by signing the Declaration of Independence.

At the statue's feet is a broken chain to symbolize that liberty means freedom.

The Statue of Liberty was a gift from France to America. But liberty itself is a gift that all people must give one another.

Chapter Two

'Tis Better to Give

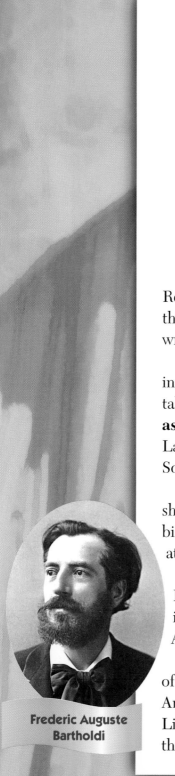

Frederic Auguste Bartholdi

T he idea to give America a gift began at a dinner party in France in 1865. Professor Edouard Rene Lefebvre de Laboulaye had written books about the United States. He was famous for his teaching and writing, as well as his dinner parties.

Laboulaye invited people to his parties to discuss life in France and around the world. He and his friends talked about the end of America's Civil War and the **assassination** of President Abraham Lincoln. Laboulaye was chairman of the French Anti-Slavery Society.

The professor thought that the people of France should give America a gift for its one hundredth birthday in 1876. He discussed his idea with the people at one of his dinners.

One of the people at this party was Frederic Auguste Bartholdi. Bartholdi was a young sculptor with a big interest in art. He thought that France's gift to America should be a giant statue.

The little group felt sure that Napoleon, the Emperor of France, wouldn't like the idea of a present for America. It was no secret that Napoleon had hoped that Lincoln would lose the Civil War. If Lincoln had lost, the United States would have split up. That would have

Napoleon Bonaparte, Emperor of France

proven that democracy didn't work. Maybe then, people like Laboulaye and his friends would stop trying to change France.

But France changed forever in 1870 when it went to war against Germany and lost. Napoleon was **exiled** to England. The new French government gave more and more liberties to its people even though Germany kept a careful watch.

Making a Dream Come True

Years after the dinner party, Laboulaye was finally able to make real plans for the gift to America. In 1871, Laboulaye rose to national power in France when he became an elected official. In 1875, he was elected to a lifetime term as a senator in France. That same year, Laboulaye organized the Franco-American Union. This group helped raise funds for the statue.

Edouard Rene Lefebvre de Laboulaye

Frederic Bartholdi, who would later build the statue, got involved in fund-raising for the project too. The French government had laws about gambling. However, a lottery was allowed to raise money for the statue. Bartholdi designed the tickets. More than 300,000 tickets were sold in three months. Cash prizes were offered. The government even donated books and artwork to give away.

While work on the statue began, banquets and an opera raised more money. Funds began to flow in when donors were offered souvenir photographs of the statue in progress. A bigger cash donation bought a bigger photograph.

Then Bartholdi created 100 clay models of the statue. Each was three feet tall. These rare collector's items brought in big money from donors.

By 1881, the Franco-American Union had raised money from more than 100,000 donors. Some estimates say that the French people raised as much as 600,000 francs. That would have equaled 450,000 American dollars at that time.

Now France needed America's help. After all, what good was an enormous statue if America had no place to put it?

Bigger Than Life

The actual height of the finished statue is 305 feet 1 inch from the tip of the torch to the bottom of the base.

Workers begin creating the statue

Chapter Three

Carving Out a Place

Visiting America

Bartholdi first visited America on June 21, 1871. He was looking for a place to put his masterpiece. In New York Harbor, he spotted Bedloe's Island.

Fort Wood had been built on the tiny island nearly 100 years before to fight the British during the American Revolutionary War. The fort's walls formed a starlike shape. Now empty, the fort could provide the support for the statue's base.

Better still, Bartholdi knew that putting his statue in the harbor would make it more than a work of art. His

New York Harbor, 1880s

tatue could also be a lighthouse. Its torch could
ffer light to ships sailing into New York Harbor.

After falling in love with Bedloe's Island,
Bartholdi wanted to tour America. He wanted to
earn about the American people to help him decide
n his statue's details. Bartholdi met with President
Ulysses S. Grant. He visited with painters, poets, and
rofessors. The sculptor spent five months in America
efore returning to France.

Finding a Home

Back home in Paris, Bartholdi kept reading
American newspapers. He learned that some New
Yorkers were unsure about having a huge statue in their
harbor. They worried about raising money for the land
nd its upkeep. The newspapers also reported,
owever, that officials in San Francisco, Philadelphia,
Boston, and Milwaukee would gladly find a site for the
tatue.

Bartholdi and the Franco-American Union had first
dreamed of giving America the statue on its one
hundredth birthday. But there was no way Bartholdi
could finish the statue in time for America's 1876
entennial. He did provide the completed arm and
orch for the celebration. This allowed Americans to
imagine the future statue.

The arm-torch combination measured 42 feet in
ength. It was displayed at the Centennial
Exposition in Philadelphia. For 50 cents, a
visitor could climb through the arm and
tand at the railing outside the frame.
The torch was previewed in
America for nearly
eight years.

Bartholdi enjoyed the Centennial Exposition and hinted to newspapers that Philadelphia might be another worthy home for the statue. But he still hoped New York would agree to let the statue sta on Bedloe's Island.

Finally, in 1877, President Grant and the Unit States Congress passed a **resolution** accepting France's gift and promising to provide an island i New York Harbor for the statue.

Liberty would have a home. But first, Bartholdi had to finish her.

Liberty Island

In 1956, Congress changed name of Bedloe's Island to Liber Island in honor of the great stat

Chapter Four

Big Dreams

W ho was this man who envisioned and built the Statue of Liberty?

Frederic Auguste Bartholdi was born in Colmar, France, in 1834. His mother took him to Paris two years later when his father died.

Bartholdi received private drawing lessons at an early age. In the 1840s, he tried taking lessons from a Dutch painter. The man told Bartholdi to become a sculptor instead.

Bartholdi and four painters traveled to Egypt and Arabia in 1855–1856. Bartholdi was impressed by the huge artwork created in ancient Egypt. One pyramid, a triangle-shaped tomb, was nearly 500 feet tall. The Great Sphinx was a statue of a man's head on a lion's body. It measured 240 feet in length and 66 feet in height. Bartholdi remembered these impressive sculptures for years to come.

Soon after his trip to Egypt, Bartholdi got the chance to create a giant sculpture of his own. In 1856, the 22-year-old sculptor was hired by his hometown to create a statue of a famous military officer. Bartholdi's sculpture stood 26 feet tall, which was an amazing height at that time.

Big Ideas

Bartholdi continued to think about creating enormous works of art. He dreamed of building a lighthouse for Egypt's Suez Canal.

For two years, he worked on a model of the statue he imagined. Bartholdi pictured a robed woman on a **pedestal**. She held out one hand in welcome. In the other hand, she raised a torch.

When the Suez Canal opened in 1869, Bartholdi traveled to

Suez Canal

The Suez Canal is a human-made waterway that connects the Mediterranean and Red Seas. The narrow canal is about 118 miles long.

the opening ceremony to present his idea. The Egyptian leader disliked the idea of a Frenchman building an important Egyptian monument.

Discouraged, Bartholdi returned to France. He found his homeland at war with Germany. Bartholdi became a soldier. When France lost the war to Germany, Bartholdi himself had to surrender his beloved hometown to the enemy.

After the war, many French people dreamed about democracy more than ever. They looked at America as a role model for their dreams. Bartholdi and his friend Laboulaye both remembered their dream of a huge statue that would represent the power of freedom. It would also show the power of friendship between France and the United States.

Bartholdi decided he would call the statue *Liberty Enlightening the World*. He prepared himself to convince the French people that the size of the gift should be enormous. "It ought to produce an emotion in the breast of the spectator—not because of its volume but because its size is in keeping with the idea that it interprets and with the place which it ought to occupy."

Bartholdi believed that liberty was a big idea worthy of big art. And because America was a place where freedom lived, Bartholdi felt America was the place for his great work of art.

"I will try to glorify the **Republic** and liberty over there in the hope that someday I will find it again here in France," he said.

Chapter Five

Starting Small

Bartholdi planned to make his final statue using a copper **repoussé** method. Copper is more flexible than stone, so moving the finished work from Paris to America would be safer.

Planning the statue involved making four models of increasing sizes. The first model was approximately four feet tall. It was carefully measured so that it could be recreated in a bigger size. The second model was made of **plaster** and wood. It stood just over nine feet tall.

As the models got larger, the statue's design changed. Details that were impossible to include on a small work were added as the models grew. Mistakes were fixed.

The third model was about 36 feet tall. The final model reached 111 feet—151 feet when the torch and arm were included.

Finding a work space for such a huge statue was almost impossible. So the final model was done in carefully measured sections.

Each section was made in plaster first. Then a wooden frame was built over and around the plaster. This made a mold. Workers pounded copper sheets as thin as silver dollars into the **crevices** of the mold until the sheets had the same shape as the plaster original. The finished hollow statue included 3,000 copper sheets.

Engineer and bridge designer Alexander Gustave Eiffel assisted in creating the inside of the Statue of Liberty. Eiffel designed an inner tower of iron nearly 97 feet high. Small iron bars attached to the tower created a skeleton. Copper sections were **riveted** to the bars to create the finished statue. The skeleton allowed the statue to move in the wind.

A Perfect Face

Bartholdi's mother, Charlotte, was the first human model for the statue. Her face is the face of Liberty. But Mrs. Bartholdi tired of standing in one position for hours. Her son chose Jeanne-Emilie Baheux de Puysieux as his next model. The sculptor and model fell in love and later got married.

An Artist's Wages

During the years Bartholdi worked on the Statue of Liberty, the French government tried to help him earn money to live on. They supported the work he was doing and wanted to make it possible for him to finish.

France hired Bartholdi to create a bronze statue of the Marquis de Lafayette clutching a sword over his heart while preparing to assist America in the American Revolutionary War. The statue was given to America in 1876 as thanks for support during the Franco-Prussian War.

Eiffel Tower

Alexander Gustave Eiffel was famous for his creation of the Eiffel Tower in 1889. This huge iron tower is located in Paris, France. For years, it was the world's highest structure at 984 feet.

Franco-Prussian War

In 1870, France and Prussia went to war over a struggle for power among European nations. Germany came to the aid of Prussia. Less than a year later, Germany overtook Paris and defeated France. The war ended with the Treaty of Frankfurt, which forced France to give land and money to Germany.

The head and shoulders of Liberty were ready by 1878. This portion of the sculpture was on display at the Paris World's Fair. For a fee, tourists could climb a set of steps and look out through openings in the statue's crown.

In 1880, France hired Bartholdi to design and supervise the carving of a mountainside statue. The *Lion of Belfort* is a 72-foot-long, 36-foot-high lion honoring French troops who fought in the Franco-Prussian War.

Even while working on other projects, Bartholdi continued building Liberty. He began calling the statue "My American." At last, in January 1884, his masterpiece was complete.

In a ceremony on July 4, 1884, the French government announced that it would pay to transport the statue to America. Levi P. Morton, the American ambassador to France, was presented with the **deed** to the statue.

But with a stormy ocean to cross, Liberty was still a long way from home.

The head of the Statue of Liberty was on display in the Champ-de-Mars during the Paris World's Fair. The Champ-de-Mars is a park in Paris, where the Eiffel Tower also stands.

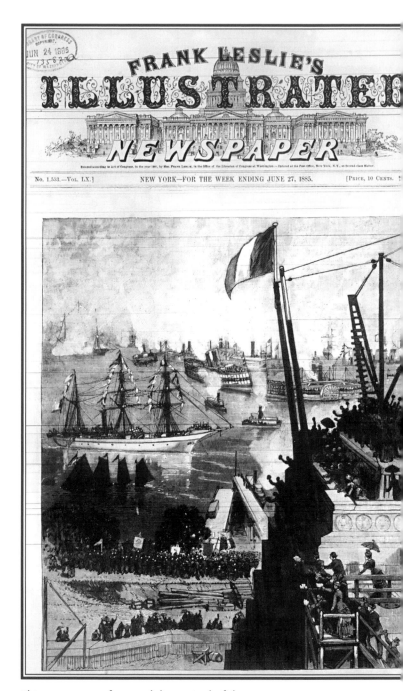

This newspaper featured the arrival of the statue.

Chapter Six

Supporting the Dream

O n May 21, 1885, the ship *Isere* set sail to America carrying 214 huge wooden boxes. The boxes contained bolts, sheets of copper, and even a stairway of 168 steps that would lead to the top of the Lady's head. All 350 pieces of the statue were packed in boxes, ready to be reassembled in America.

Everyone hoped the statue would arrive in about a week. But the *Isere* was delayed by a huge storm at sea. The ship did not arrive until mid-June—almost a month after departure.

Tipping the Scales

Lady Liberty weighs 450,000 pounds.

Some Americans worried about the statue's safe arrival. Others worried about what would happen if Liberty *did* arrive. A spot still needed to be prepared for her permanent display. How much would that cost? How much would it cost to put the sculpture back together? More importantly, where would all the money come from?

THE BARTHOLDI STATUE.
Even Liberty demands something substantial to stand upon.

Funds for Freedom

President Grover Cleveland vetoed a bill that would have provided $100,000 in **federal** money. The president's decision reflected the feelings of some Americans. Such critics said that New Yorkers should pay for the statue since it would be located in their state.

One newspaper teased that money could be raised by renting advertising space on the huge statue.

Instead, a fund-raising committee called the American Committee of the Franco-American Union asked citizens to donate money. Led by New York lawyer William Evarts, the group sold six-inch bronzed statues of the Statue of Liberty. These one-dollar souvenirs showed

Liberty standing on her not-yet-completed pedestal. Advertisements claimed that each model was "proof of title to ownership in this great work." Owners of the statue could feel proud that they had contributed to the real Statue of Liberty.

Of the People, For the People

The publisher of the *New York World* newspaper challenged all of his readers to donate to the statue. Publisher Joseph Pulitzer promised that he'd print the names of everyone who contributed. Pulitzer wrote, "Let us not wait for the millionaires to give the money. This isn't a gift from French millionaires to American millionaires." Pulitzer wrote that ordinary French workers wanted *all* Americans to enjoy the statue.

On August 11, 1885, Pulitzer printed a cartoon on the front page of his newspaper. In the cartoon, Lady Liberty was waving a flag and holding a bag of donated money. Uncle Sam was painting an **inscription** on the statue's

pedestal. The words read, "This pedestal to Liberty was provided by the voluntary contributions of 120,000 patriotic citizens of the American Union through the *New York World*."

Who Is Uncle Sam?

Uncle Sam is an imaginary figure who symbolizes the United States. He was created during the War of 1812 when "Uncle Sam" was used as a negative nickname for the U.S. government. The name "Uncle Sam" comes from the initials U.S. (United States). Although his appearance has changed over the years, Uncle Sam is usually decorated in a costume of stars and stripes.

Thanks in large part to Pulitzer's urging, $102,000 was raised to support the assembly of the Statue of Liberty.

Putting the Pieces Together

The crates holding the pieces of Liberty sat unopened on Bedloe's Island for nearly two months. Finally enough money was raised to put the statue together and build a pedestal. The designer of the pedestal, Richard Morris Hunt, even donated his $1,000 fee to the fund-raising effort.

Once the pedestal was built, it took about four months

o reassemble the statue. Bartholdi spent three weeks in America coordinating the construction. More than a year after her arrival in New York, the Lady of Liberty was finally complete.

A Dream Come True

On October 28, 1886, one million people lined the rainy streets of New York. Some 20,000 marchers celebrated the dedication of the statue.

On Bedloe's Island, more than 2,000 government leaders and guests from France and America were invited for the unveiling. Only two women attended the ceremony.

Bartholdi waited in Liberty's crown, ready to pull the cord that would remove a French flag from the statue's face after President Grover Cleveland's speech. However, Bartholdi got confused and removed the flag before the president had spoken a word!

The mistake didn't ruin the proud day. Speeches and songs saluted the new landmark. President Cleveland told Bartholdi, "You are the greatest man in America today!"

Bartholdi told reporters, "The dream of my life is accomplished."

Death Before Dedication

Edouard de Laboulaye, the man who first thought of America's gift, was not at the Statue of Liberty's dedication. He died on May 25, 1883, without seeing his vision rise in America.

NEW YORK.—THE UNVAILING OF THE BARTHOLDI STATUE OF LIBERTY, OCTOBER 28TH.—PRESIDENT CLEVELAND PASSING THROUGH THE FLEET OF ASSEMBLED VESSELS IN THE LAUNCH "VIXEN," ON HIS WAY TO BEDLOW'S ISLAND. THE GRAND SALUTE.

FROM A SKETCH BY A STAFF ARTIST.—SEE PAGE 182.

Chapter Seven

I Lift My Lamp

The people came and the Lady welcomed them. The Statue of Liberty came to New York at the same time millions of other **immigrants** arrived. People from all over the world came to live in America, the land of the free. They traveled by ship, often passing through New York Harbor.

One of the first things these immigrants saw in the United States was the Statue of Liberty. This Lady who represented freedom and the right to choose was a welcome sight to those escaping poverty and **persecution**.

The Statue of Liberty greets immigrants in New York Harbor.

Starting in 1892, immigrants were taken to nearby Ellis Island for physicals and interviews for **citizenship** applications.

All the while, Lady Liberty seemed to watch over them.

Some immigrants knew the history of the statue. Others thought she must be a religious saint. But who could dislike her? She was American like they longed to be.

Immigrant children arriving on Ellis Island

In 1903, a poem was added to the statue's pedestal. The words seemed to be spoken by the Lady herself. They welcomed immigrants to America.

The New Colossus

Not like the brazen giant of Greek fame,
With conquering limbs astride from land to land;
Here at our sea-washed, sunset gates shall stand
A mighty woman with a torch, whose flame
Is the imprisoned lightning, and her name
Mother of Exiles. From her beacon-hand
Glows world-wide welcome; her mild eyes command
The air-bridged harbor that twin cities frame.
"Keep ancient lands, your storied pomp!" cries she
With silent lips. "Give me your tired, your poor,
Your huddled masses yearning to breathe free,
The wretched refuse of your teeming shore.
Send these, the homeless, tempest-tost to me,
I lift my lamp beside the golden door!"

The poem, "The New **Colossus**," was written by
Emma Lazarus. Lazarus wrote the words after meeting
Jews who had been mistreated in Russia. They had fled
to America in search of a better life. Lazarus was Jewish
too. She used her poem to help raise funds for the
statue's pedestal in 1883.

Sadly, Lazarus died of cancer in 1884 before Lady
Liberty arrived in New York. She was only 38 years old.
The poet may not have lived to see her poem engraved
on the pedestal, but her words are yet another symbol of
the statue and its true meaning.

earning To Breathe Free

More than 12 million immigrants became Americans by passing
ough the Ellis Island Immigration Center. Only two percent of
immigrants who came to America were rejected as citizens. The
who weren't granted citizenship often had major illnesses.

The immigration center at Ellis Island closed in 1954. According
government studies, seven out of every ten immigrants who
ame Americans by 1954 came through Ellis Island.

In 1954, President Dwight D. Eisenhower encouraged the
ilding of an American Museum of Immigration. As with the
tue of Liberty, money was a problem. The museum was not
ded, completed, and opened until 1972.

The museum was first located beneath the statue itself. One of
museum's rooms honored the building of the Statue of Liberty.

In 1991, the immigration museum beneath the statue was closed.
ew, expanded museum opened on the newly remodeled Ellis
nd. More than one million tourists visit the new museum each
r.

When Lady Liberty came to America, she came by ship like most
migrants did at the time. Today's immigrants don't have to come
ship. Not as many of them will see the statue symbolizing
edom. But many will know she's there, holding her lamp to
lcome them.

Chapter Eight

The Tests of Time

P lans for the Statue of Liberty's birthday party began early. Everyone knew that the statue would be 100 years old in 1986.

However, plans for the celebration were overshadowed by concerns about the statue's condition. Lady Liberty was showing her age. Wind, rain, hail, snow, and air pollution had all caused damage to Miss Liberty. Would she survive another 100 years?

In 1981, French engineers volunteered to help study the **restoration** needs of the statue. The following year, President Ronald Reagan formed a commission to plan for the repair of the Statue of Liberty and Ellis Island.

Even though Ellis Island's one hundredth birthday wouldn't arrive until 1992, the plan was to raise money to repair both sites. The Statue of Liberty and Ellis Island were related landmarks for American immigrants.

Estimates said that $200 million would be needed to restore Ellis Island. The Statue of Liberty would require

30 million. Once again, where would the money come from?

Looking After Liberty

Lee Iacocca, chairman of the Chrysler car company, agreed to lead the commission. Iacocca's parents had passed by the statue on their way to Ellis Island decades earlier when they'd immigrated from Italy. Iacocca estimated that 100 million Americans had relatives who had first entered America by ship, passing the Statue of Liberty on the way to Ellis Island.

The worst part about restoring Lady Liberty was that she would have to be closed from 1984 to 1986.

The restoration began with the building of an aluminum **scaffolding** for workers to stand on. This 300-foot framework surrounded Lady Liberty. From far away, it looked as if the statue were in jail!

The top 150 feet of the frame was 18 inches away from the statue. Because the statue swayed slightly in high winds, gusts could have toppled workers who were too close.

High-pressure water hoses blasted stains and bird droppings from the statue's copper skin. Every one of the statue's 12,000 **rivets** were replaced. The interior iron skeleton was replaced as well.

One tricky part of the restoration was Lady Liberty's "nose job." One nostril needed to be replaced. A mold was made of the original, and a replacement was shaped using the copper repoussé method.

All seven rays of Liberty's crown were removed and cleaned. Some small rips in the statue's thin copper sheets were hammered back together.

Workers were careful not to remove the blue-green **patina** that Liberty's copper had acquired through the years. When it was new, Liberty had the light brown coloring of a copper penny. The color change came from age and weather. The greenish coating actually protects the metal from more rust.

The statue's torch was removed on July 4, 1984. A new torch was mounted in 1986. The new gold flame does not light from within. Its glow comes from a ring of spotlights shining on it.

At last, in 1986, Lady Liberty was given a grand party just like the celebration 100 years before. Both American President Ronald Reagan and French President Francois Mitterrand gave speeches. A century later, the idea of liberty still united the two countries.

President Ronald Reagan gave a speech at the centennial of the Statue of Liberty in 1986.

Chapter Nine

Liberty Unafraid

Throughout the years, the Statue of Liberty has faced many dangers. The Lady has survived these threats with grace and dignity.

Explosion!

On July 30, 1916, a train car loaded with **ammunition** exploded in nearby New Jersey. The train yard there was full of dynamite waiting to be shipped to England and France for use in World War I. More than 20 years later, evidence suggested that German spies created the explosion.

Liberty's copper outsides were scraped by flying **debris**. The blast loosened 100 rivets that held copper in place on the statue's right arm. Visitors were no longer allowed to climb all the way inside the statue to the torch.

The repairs cost $100,000. Sculptor Gutzon Borglum was asked to fix the statue's torch. Trying to help, Borglum added 250 panes of glass to Liberty's torch. He cut away copper from the top of the torch, hoping more light would escape. Instead, years of rain flowed into the opening, **corroding** the metal.

A Long Reach!

Lady Liberty's right arm is 42 feet long.

A Success Story

While he may not have been appreciated for his work on Liberty's torch, Gutzon Borglum was definitely appreciated for his creation of Mount Rushmore. Located in South Dakota, this mountainside sculpture portrays the faces of four American presidents. Like the Statue of Liberty, Mount Rushmore is a huge sculpture designed to symbolize America's greatness.

Put Out That Torch!

During World War II, the statue's torch was not lit at night. From 1942 to 1945, American cities practiced blackouts at night. All unneeded lights were turned off or hidden behind thick curtains. That way, enemy aircraft couldn't see where to drop bombs. Darkening Liberty's torch was another way to hide the city at night.

One wartime exception was made at midnight on New Year's Eve in 1943. The statue torch blinked three quick blinks followed by one long flash. In **Morse code**, that was the signal for the letter V. Americans knew that V stood for "victory." Victory would mean an end to the war.

Peace Protests

People have often come to the Statue of Liberty to protest against wars. Protesters feel that this statue representing freedom and acceptance helps them to be seen and heard.

On November 5, 2000, National Park Service police reported that a group of six people were protesting the presence of the U.S. military on the Puerto Rican island of Vieques. The demonstrators climbed to the observation area in Liberty's crown and broke out a window. One man scrambled out to the exterior deck and unfurled the flags of Puerto Rico and Vieques as well as two banners reading "Peace" and "Vieques."

Playing with Fire

In 2000, the New York City Fire Department found that only one fire hydrant existed on Liberty Island. Worse yet, the National Park Service (NPS) had known about the hazard for at least two years, but nothing had been done.

The NPS had completed a safety study of the statue in 1998. The results stated that getting people safely off the stairways and out of the statue would be difficult if the statue suddenly filled with smoke. Staff working at the statue were not trained firefighters. The New York City firefighters would need at least 15 minutes to reach Liberty Island by boat. The study concluded that "there i a high probability of life loss and severe injury" in case of fire or smoke.

Why hadn't anything been done about the problem? NPS officials said there had never been a fire at the statu in its first 114 years. The risk didn't seem high.

But after the fire department noticed the problem, newspapers reported the hazard. Less than a week after these articles came out, the NPS pledged $800,000 to improve fire safety at the statue.

Dangerous Skies

Miss Liberty received a surprise visitor on August 23, 2001. A French stuntman with a gasoline-powered engin strapped to his back tried to fly onto the statue so he could bungee jump from it. Unfortunately his plan changed when his parachute snagged on the torch.

Fearing the statue was under attack, police **evacuated** tourists. But 41-year-old Thierry Devaux was only a daredevil with bad luck. He dangled helplessly for nearly 45 minutes before being rescued—and arrested. He was ordered to pay $7,000 in fines.

Less than one month later, on September 11, 2001, terrorists hijacked and crashed planes into New York City's World Trade Center. Fearing more attacks, the National Park Service closed the statue and Liberty Island.

The island finally reopened more than three months later, although no visitors were allowed inside the statue. Still, tourists came. They walked around the statue, admiring the fearless Lady of Liberty. She looked to sea as she always had—to the unknown, to the future, to the world.

A Statue of Monumental Importance

The Statue of Liberty became a National Monument on October 15, 1924. As such, it is protected and taken care of by the National Park Service.

Internet Connections to the Statue of Liberty

http://www.endex.com/gf/buildings/liberty/liberty.html
Check out facts, news, and information about the Statue of Liberty at this site. Enjoy a gallery of photos showing both inside and outside views of the statue.

http://www.sccorp.com/cam/default.htm
This Statue of Liberty cam provides updated pictures of the statue 24 hours a day. Visit the Web site at sunrise or sunset for the clearest views.

http://www.nyctourist.com/liberty1.htm
Take an online tour of the journey to and through the Statue of Liberty. Beginning with the ferry ride from Battery Park, you will experience a trip to Liberty Island through pictures and descriptions. It's almost like being there!

http://www.nps.gov/stli/
This is the official Statue of Liberty National Monument site sponsored by the National Park Service. The NPS oversees the statue on Liberty Island, as well as Ellis Island. Preview information about what you can see at both locations.

http://www.terrydo.com/english/frame/frame_a.htm
Thierry Devaux, who calls himself Terry Dô, is the French stuntman who was arrested for trying to bungee jump from the Statue of Liberty. Here he explains his performance on Liberty Island. He also tells about his Eiffel Tower adventure.

ammunition	explosive items
assassination	murder
centennial	hundredth birthday or anniversary
citizenship	membership to a country or community
colossus	statue of gigantic size
corroding	wearing away by chemical action
crevice	narrow opening
debris	remains of something destroyed
deed	paper that shows ownership of something
democracy	government in which the people elect representatives
evacuated	removed from a dangerous situation
exiled	forced to leave a country
federal	relating to the central government of a country
immigrant	person moving to one country from another one
inscription	words that are written, engraved, or printed on an object

Morse code	system of dots and dashes used to send messages
patina	film that forms naturally on copper
pedestal	base or foundation
persecution	suffering or harassment due to differences in race, religion, beliefs, etc.
plaster	pasty mixture that hardens when it dries
repoussé	process of hammering metal over a mold to shape it
republic	country with elected representatives
resolution	formal agreement voted on by an elected group
restoration	returning to original condition
revolution	fighting to overthrow a government
rivet	small metal pin
riveted	attached with small metal pins
scaffolding	system of temporary or movable platforms for workers

Immigrants waiting in line at Ellis Island,

Index

American Committee of the Franco-American Union, 24

American Museum of Immigration, 33

American Revolutionary War, 6

Bartholdi, Charlotte, 19

Bartholdi, Frederic Auguste, 8, 10, 12–14, 15–17, 19–21

Bedloe's Island (Liberty Island), 12–13, 14, 26, 27

Borglum, Gutzon, 38–39

Centennial Exposition, 13–14

Cleveland, Grover, 24, 27

Devaux, Thierry, 40, 43

Egypt, 16–17

Eiffel Tower, 19, 21

Eiffel, Alexander Gustave, 19

Eisenhower, Dwight D., 33

Ellis Island, 30, 33, 34, 35

Evarts, William, 24

fire hazards, 40

Fort Wood, 12

Franco-American Union, 9–10, 13

Franco-Prussian War, 19

French Revolution, 6

fund–raising, 9–10, 23–26

Grant, Ulysses S., 13, 14

Hunt, Richard Morris, 26

Iacocca, Lee, 35

immigration, 29–33

Isere, 22–23

Lafayette, Marquis de, 5, 19

Laboulaye, Edouard Rene Lefebvre de, 8–9, 27

Lazarus, Emma, 31

Liberty Enlightening the World, 17

liberty (definition of), 4

Lincoln, Abraham, 8

Lion of Belfort, 20

Mitterrand, Francois, 36

models (of the statue), 18–19

Morton, Levi P., 21

Napoleon, 8–9

National Park Service, 40, 41, 42, 43

"New Colossus, The", 30–31

New York Harbor, 12–13, 14

Paris World's Fair, 20–21

peace protests, 39

Puerto Rico, 39

Pulitzer, Joseph, 25–26

Pulitzer Prize, 25

Puysieux, Jeanne-Emilie
        Baheux de, 19

Reagan, Ronald, 34, 36–37

Statue of Liberty
        chain, 7
        crown, 7, 20, 36
        dedication, 27, 28
        movement in wind, 19, 36
        restoration, 34–36
        size, 7, 10, 13, 20, 23, 36, 38
        tablet, 7
        torch, 7, 36

Statue of Liberty National
        Monument, 42

Suez Canal, 16–17

train explosion, 38

Uncle Sam, 25–26

Vieques, 39

Washington, George, 5

World Trade Center, 41

World War II, 39